GW00384724

THE TWINS IN FRANCE

Sally Kilroy

ORCHARD BOOKS

London

We're going to France for a camping holiday. Ben and I are helping to load the car.

"Does Mum really think we need all this, Katie?" asks Dad.

We cross the English Channel to France in a big ferry.
When we arrive, we have to show our passports.
"*Merci*," the passport man says to Dad as he hands
them back. I can say that too; it means 'thank you'.

Dad drives off on the wrong side of the road! But Mum
tells us everyone drives on the right in France.

We come to a little town and Dad wants to stop for coffee.

In the café Mum tries out her French. "*Deux cafés au lait et deux limonades, s'il vous plait.*" She is pleased when the waitress understands her.

After we've had our drinks Ben says, "I'm hungry."

So we go and buy some food for lunch. In the baker's we get two *baguettes*, long crusty white loaves.

Next door we buy pâté and cheese. Further up the street is a *pâtisserie* which sells wonderful strawberry tarts.

We have our picnic near a canal. A big barge goes slowly by and a lady at the back waves at me.

"*Bonjour!*" I shout to her. That means 'good morning'.

Dad spreads out the rug on the edge of a sweetcorn field. I've never seen corn on the cob growing before!

We all help put out the food. Ben and I can't wait to have our strawberry tarts.

Late in the afternoon we come to a vineyard. There's a
huge tractor spraying the grapes.

Mum and Dad go into the wine cellar to taste the wine.
Ben and I are allowed to have a tiny sip too. Ugh! it's all
bitter! But Mum and Dad seem to like it!

At last we arrive at our camp site. We've got a big tent that's even got a cooker and a fridge in it.

But we have to go to another building to wash before bed. We don't know which way to go in until a lady comes out of the door marked *Dames!*

Next day we look at the map and try to decide what to do.

Ben would like to stay and play football with his new French friend, Pierre.

But we all set off in the car to visit a little town right on top of a hill.

We leave the car outside the walls and walk up a
cobbled street into the town.

In the town centre a policeman keeps blowing his whistle at a car that has gone the wrong way.

The old narrow streets are very noisy. Cars and mopeds zoom past and we must be careful to look to the left first before we cross the roads.

It's market day! Brightly-coloured stalls fill the main square of the town. We wander round to see what

everyone's selling and we buy some cheese for lunch.
Ben wants to take one of the white rabbits home with him.

Mum and Dad have to go to the bank to change travellers cheques into francs.

Ben and I buy two postcards from the lady at the newspaper stall. We're not sure which coins to use so she helps us count out the right money.

Then we have to go to the tobacconist's shop to get stamps.

After lunch everything seems to go quiet and most of the shops shut.

But an ice-cream stall in the square is still open. There are so many different flavours, I don't know which to have.

Ben asks for a nutty green one called *pistache* and finally I choose *fraise* which tastes of strawberries. It's delicious!

Afterwards we write our postcards, one to Grandma and one to our friend Minty. Then we post them.

One hot day we visit an abbey. Inside it's cool and we
have to talk in whispers.

Soon Ben and I get tired of being quiet. We find a doorway to a lovely garden with pillars all around. I play hide and seek. Ben climbs on to an old stone seat and pretends he's a king.

On Sunday we watch a game called *boules* in the village square. One of the players lets us have a go. We have to throw the large metal balls as close as we can to the small one. It's difficult!

On the last evening of the holiday we all go out for a meal. In the restaurant Mum has to use her phrase book to help read the menu.

"*Escargots*... snails," says Mum. "Ooh, I couldn't." But Dad tries them and quite enjoys the taste.

Ben and I have chicken with chips called *pommes frites*.

It's long past our bedtime when Ben and I wriggle into our sleeping bags.

"What did you like best about France?" I ask.

"Playing football with Pierre," Ben murmurs sleepily.

I liked everything, even though France is quite different from England.